ZOO!

A Book of Poems

ZOO!
A Book of Poems

selected by Lee Bennett Hopkins

pictures by Robert Frankenberg

Crown Publishers, Inc. New York

 Inquiries should be addressed to Crown Publishers, Inc., 419 Park Avenue South, New York, N.Y. 10016. Printed in the United States of America. Library of Congress Catalog Card Number: 76-147347. Published simultaneously in Canada by General Publishing Company Limited.

ACKNOWLEDGMENTS

Thanks are due to the following authors and publishers for permission to use the material included:

Atheneum Publishers for "Balloons" from *Catch Me a Wind,* copyright © 1968 by Patricia Hubbell. Used by permission of Atheneum Publishers.

E. P. Dutton and Company, Inc., for "Afterthought" and "A Monkey," from the book *Rhymes About the City,* by Marchette Chute. Copyright 1946 by Marchette Chute. Reprinted by the permission of the author.

Follett Publishing Company for "Necks," from *The Day Is Dancing,* by Rowena Bennett. Text copyright 1948, 1968 by Rowena Bennett. Used by permission of Follett Publishing Company.

Grosset and Dunlap, Inc., for "Yowl Owl (Junior)" reprinted from *Various Owls,* by John Hollander. Copyright © 1963 by John Hollander. A W. W. Norton book published by Grosset and Dunlap, Inc.

Harcourt, Brace, Jovanovich, Inc., for "If You Find a Little Feather," from *Something Special,* copyright © 1958 by Beatrice Schenk de Regniers. "At the Zoo" from *Whispers and Other Poems,* copyright © 1958 by Myra Cohn Livingston. "In This Jungle," from *A Crazy Flight and Other Poems,* copyright © 1969 by Myra Cohn Livingston. All reprinted by permission of Harcourt, Brace, Jovanovich, Inc.

Harlin Quist, Inc., for "Hippopotamus" and "Polar Bear" by Gail Kredenser from *The ABC's of Bumptious Beasts,* copyright © 1966 by Harlin Quist, Inc. Reprinted by permission of the publisher.

Harper and Row Publishers, Inc., for "Pete at the Zoo" from *The Bean Eaters* by Gwendolyn Brooks. Copyright © 1960 by Gwendolyn Brooks. Reprinted by permission of Harper and Row Publishers, Inc.

Lee Bennett Hopkins for "Mr. Zookeeper," copyright © 1970, 1971 by Lee Bennett Hopkins, and "To the Zoo," copyright © 1971 by Lee Bennett Hopkins.

Bobbi Katz for "Llama" and "Matilda," copyright © 1971 by Bobbi Katz.

Larry Kirkman for "The Balloon Man," copyright © 1971 by Larry Kirkman.

J. B. Lippincott Company for "People Buy a Lot of Things" from the book *For Days and Days* by Annette Wynne. Copyright © 1919 by J. B. Lippincott Company. Renewal 1947 by Annette Wynne. Reprinted by permission of the publishers.

G. P. Putnam's Sons for "Supper for a Lion" from *All Together* by Dorothy Aldis. Copyright © 1925, 1926, 1927, 1928, 1934, 1952, 1959. Reprinted by permission of G. P. Putnam's Sons.

Random House, Inc., for "Here She Is," from *Give A Guess* by Mary Britton Miller. Copyright © 1957 by Pantheon Books, Inc., a division of Random House, Inc. Reprinted by permission of the publisher.

For Charles
who has a tiger
LBH

Contents

TO THE ZOO

I'm going to the zoo
with you
with you.
I'll try to stalk a lion
and ride a kangaroo.

Then I'll climb a tall giraffe
and laugh.
And laugh and laugh
and LAUGH!

When I've had enough of zoo
I'll leave it and go home
with you
with you
with you.

Lee Bennett Hopkins

IN THIS JUNGLE

In this jungle
I will search an elephant,
A huge elephant, gray, with pink eyes.

It is quiet now,
But I understand
That if I listen carefully,
If I crouch very still,
If I wait patiently,
He will come.

Boughs break.
Feet thunder.
Branches fly.
And there will be a world of trumpeting

When he comes.
When my elephant comes.

Myra Cohn Livingston

MATILDA

Matilda, the mouse in the elephant house,
Is someone you rarely will see.
There's no sign to say:

FOR MICE—GO THIS WAY!

So how could you know *where* she'll be?

Bobbi Katz

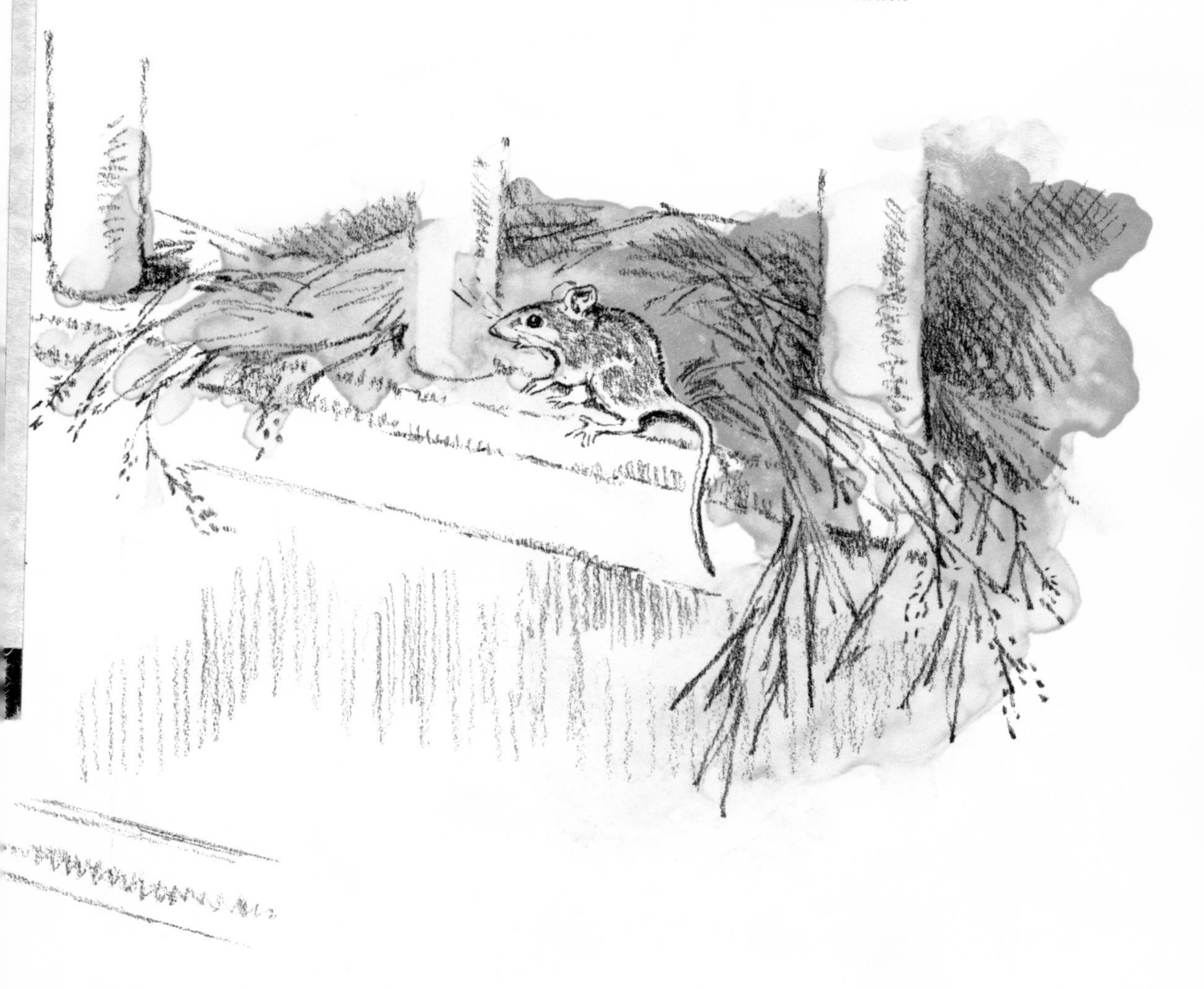

HIPPOPOTAMUS

Hooray for the hippopotamus—
A most enormous beast;
He looks as though he's eaten
Just a little too much yeast.

His mouth would dwarf a canyon
(And that's the honest truth!) –
Why, it takes three dozen dentists
Just to pull a hippo's tooth.

Gail Kredenser

LLAMA

Visitor from far Peru,
Tell us what's amusing you.
Your quiet smile just seems to say
You're thinking of a joke to play.

Bobbi Katz

POLAR BEAR

The secret of the polar bear
Is that he wears long underwear.

Gail Kredenser

NECKS

The swan has a neck that is curly and long.
The camel has one that is shaggy and strong.
But the spotted giraffe
Has a neck and a half.

Rowena Bennett

SUPPER FOR A LION

Savage lion in the zoo,
Walking by on padded feet,
To and fro and fro and to,
You seem to think it's time to eat.

Then how about a bowl of stew
With Jell-O for dessert? Or would
A juicy bone be best for you?

Oh, please don't stare
as though you knew
That I'd taste good!

Dorothy Aldis

HERE SHE IS

Jungle necklaces are hung
Around her tiger throat
And on her tiger arms are slung
Bracelets black and brown;
She shows off when she lies down
All her tiger strength and grace,
You can see the tiger blaze
In her tiger eyes, her tiger face.

Mary Britton Miller

A MONKEY

He likes to sit
With head in hand
 Upon his little shelf,
A feeling I
Can understand.
 I think a lot myself.

Marchette Chute

YOWL OWL
(Junior)

The sunset's dying:
An owl keeps crying.
Is it maybe
Because he's a baby?

John Hollander

THE BALLOON MAN

Balloons hold up his tired arm.
He rests on a box.
So tired,
His eyes shut.

He would like to float away.

Larry Kirkman

LLAMA
DO NOT FEED
THE ANIMALS

BALLOONS

Pop!

POP!

POp!

pop

y i n g

l o o n l

l s w e r e f

a

B

What can we do with them? What can we do with them?

What can we do with the dead balloons?
Nothing! Nothing!
No thing can we do with them.
Only remember them, think and remember them.
That is the way of the bright balloons.

Patricia Hubbell

MR. ZOOKEEPER

Mr. Zookeeper,
You hold the key
To let all the animals run away free.

You can send them back
    to their African plain
Let them race through the jungle
    in the sun and the rain.

But, come to think of it,
If you do,
We'll be the only ones left
    in an empty zoo!

Lee Bennett Hopkins

AFTERTHOUGHT

There's many animals at the Zoo,
And there's a place for eating, too.

Marchette Chute

PEOPLE BUY A LOT OF THINGS

People buy a lot of things—
Carts and balls and nails and rings,
But I would buy a bird that sings.

I would buy a bird that sings and let it sing for me,
And let it sing of flying things and mating in a tree,
And then I'd open wide the cage, and set the singer free.

Annette Wynne

IF YOU FIND A LITTLE FEATHER

If you find a little feather,
a little white feather,
a soft and tickly feather,
    it's for you.

A feather is a letter
from a bird,
and it says,
"Think of me.
Do not forget me.
Remember me always.
Remember me forever.
Or remember me
at least
until
the little feather
is
lost."

So . . .

. . . if you find a little feather
a little white feather,
a soft and tickly feather,
    it's for you.
        Pick it up
        and . . .
          put it in your pocket!

Beatrice Schenk de Regniers

LEX. AVE

AT THE ZOO

I've been to the zoo
where the thing that you do
is watching the things
that the animals do—

and watching
the animals
all watching
you!

Myra Cohn Livingston

PETE AT THE ZOO

I wonder if the elephant
Is lonely in his stall
When all the boys and girls are gone
And there's no shout at all,
And there's no one to stamp before,
No one to note his might.
Does he hunch up, as I do,
Against the dark of night?

Gwendolyn Brooks